Puberty, Reproduction & Birth

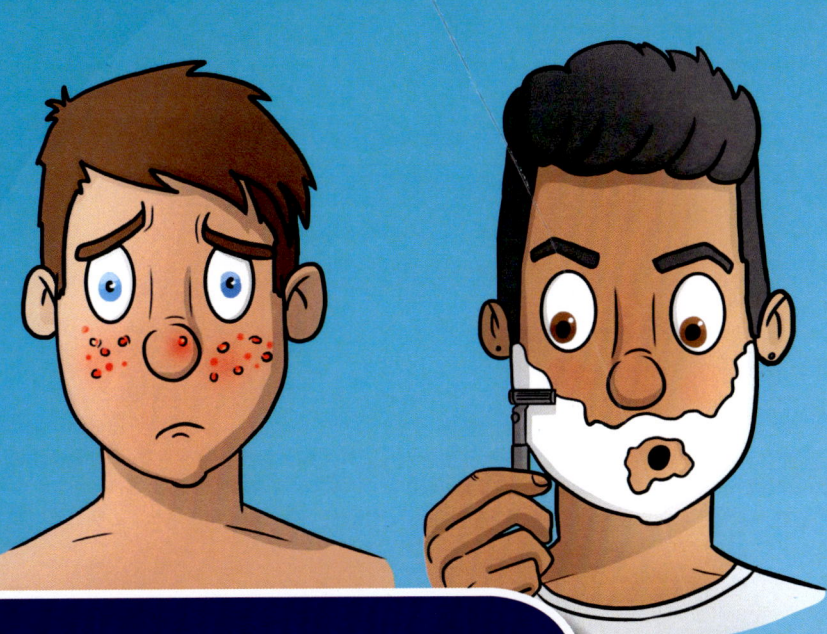

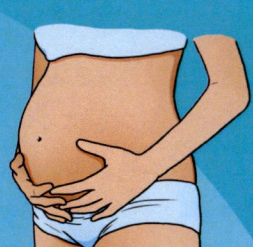

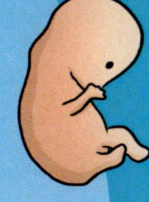

- Read, engage and learn!
- Full colour, illustrated Topic Booklet.
- Glossary, Memory Map, Active Learning Game & Flashcards.
- Ideal for Common Entrance and KS3 pupils.

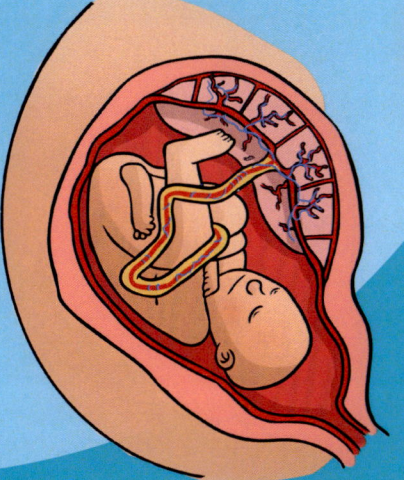

This Oaka™ Books Topic Booklet goes hand in hand with the Active Learning Pack on this topic. The pack includes a Write Your Own Notes Booklet, an Active Learning Game and Question & Answer Flashcards.

Fresh Focus on Learning

Puberty, Reproduction & Birth Glossary

 **Acne (ak-nee):** red spots on the skin, mainly on the face.

 **Adulthood:** a person who has reached sexual maturity.

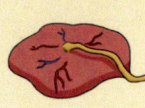 **Afterbirth:** the placenta leaving the womb after a baby is born.

 **Birth:** a baby being born.

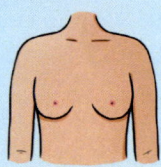 **Breasts:** organs of the upper chest in females. They produce milk after giving birth.

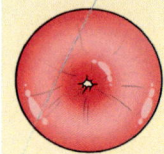 **Cervix:** a tough muscle that is usually closed, but opens during birth.

 **Childhood:** the time before puberty.

 **Ejaculation:** the action of ejecting semen from the male body.

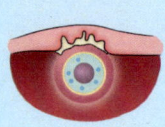 **Embryo (em-bree-owe):** a fertilised egg which develops into an unborn baby.

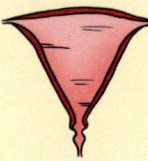 **Endometrium (en-doe-meet-ree-um):** the membrane that lines the womb.

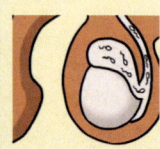 **Epididymis (ep-ee-did-ee-mis):** where sperm moves from to ejaculate.

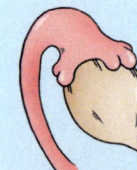 **Fallopian Tube:** the tube an egg passes through from an ovary.

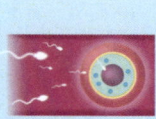 **Fertilisation (fer-til-eyes-ay-shon):** the moment where a sperm and an egg join together.

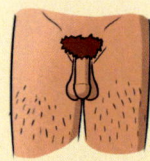 **Genitals:** a person's organs of reproduction. Can be male or female.

 **Growth Spurt:** a rapid increase in growth which happens during puberty.

 **Hormones:** chemical substances in the body that influence moods.

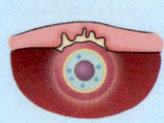 **Implantation:** where a fertilised egg attaches to the lining of the uterus.

 **Menopause:** when menstruation no longer happens.

Puberty, Reproduction & Birth Glossary

 **Menstruation (men-stroo-ay-shon):** an unfertilised egg being bled out each month.

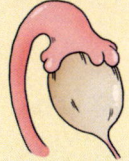 **Oestrogen (ee-str-ow-gen):** female hormone found in the ovaries.

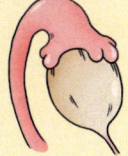 **Ovaries:** a female reproductive organ that produces human egg cells.

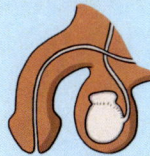 **Penis:** the male reproductive organ.

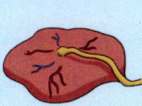 **Placenta (pla-sen-ter):** an organ that gives nutrients to an unborn baby.

 **Puberty:** where children reach sexual maturity and can reproduce.

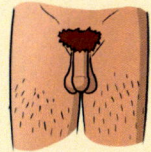 **Pubic Hair:** hair that surrounds the genitals of a person.

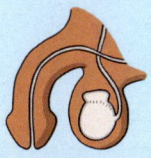 **Scrotum:** a pouch of skin that contains the testicles.

 **Semen:** sperm cells mixed with solutions when ejaculated.

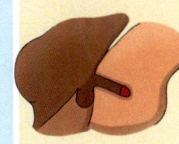 **Sexual Intercourse:** the insertion of an erect penis into a vagina, where ejaculation will occur.

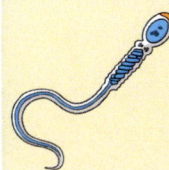 **Sperm Cell:** made in the testes. It contains half of the genetic information needed for a baby.

 **Testes:** produce sperm. Found in the scrotum.

 **Testosterone (test-oss-ter-own):** male hormones produced in the testes.

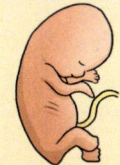 **Umbilical Cord:** the cord connecting the fetus to the placenta, giving nutrients.

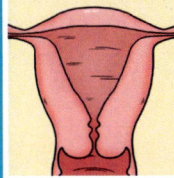 **Uterus (you-ter-us):** a womb that provides a safe place for a growing fetus.

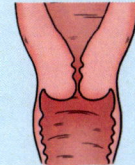 **Vagina:** outer part of the female reproductive system.

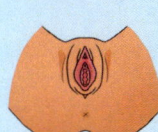 **Vulva:** external tissue folds that hide the opening of the vagina.

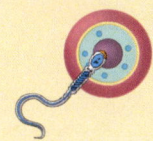 **Zygote (zz-eye-got):** the result of a sperm fertilising a human egg cell.

Puberty

1   Puberty

- During puberty, **physical and emotional changes** start.

- This is the process of you becoming ready for sex and parenthood.

- It is the change from childhood to **adulthood**.

2   Hormones

- Chemicals are released from your brain.

- These stimulate your testes or ovaries.

- These chemicals are called **hormones**.

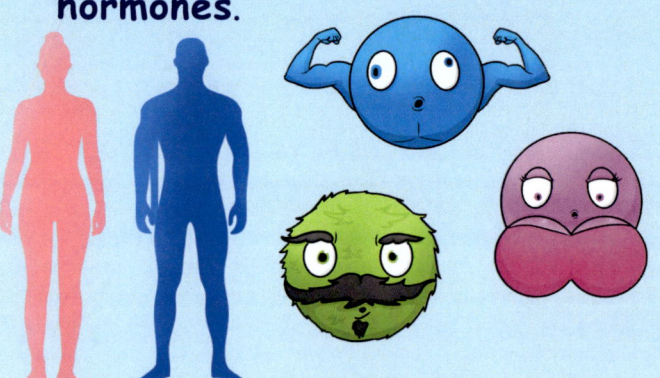

3   Testosterone (test-oss-ter-own)

- **In boys**, puberty usually starts between **12 and 14 years old**.

- It can last up to 4 years.

- It begins when the hormone, **testosterone** is released from the testes.

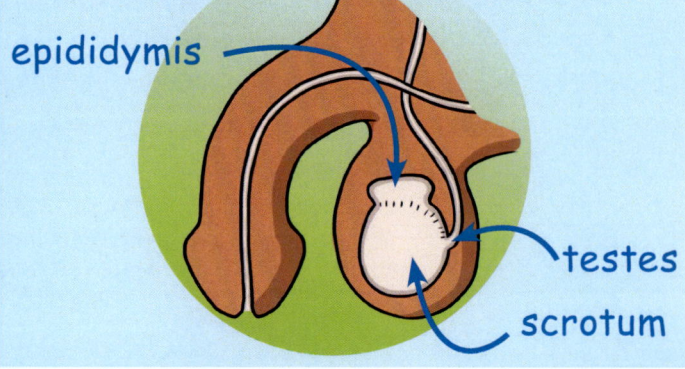

epididymis

testes

scrotum

4   Oestrogen (ee-str-ow-gen)

- **In girls**, puberty usually starts between **10 and 12 years old** and lasts up to 4 years.

- It starts when the hormone, **oestrogen** is released from the ovaries.

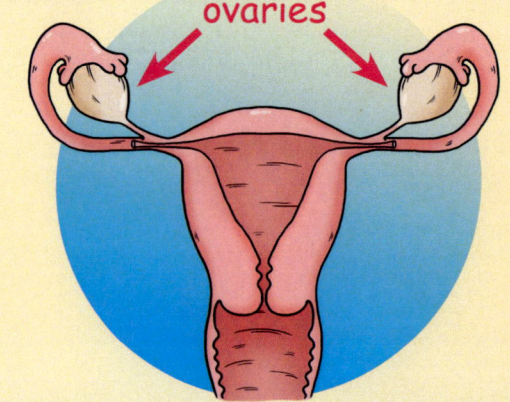

ovaries

Changes in Males

5   Physical Changes in Boys

Part 1:

- Testes grow.
- Pubic hair grows around the gentials.

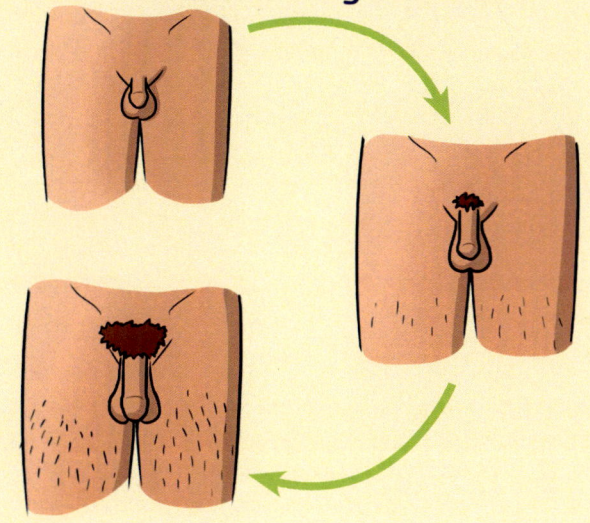

6   Physical Changes in Boys

Part 2:

- Penis lengthens.
- Wet dreams may happen.
- Voice deepens.
- Muscles get bigger.
- Growth spurt.

7   Physical Changes in Boys

Part 3:

- Hair under arms.
- Acne may develop.
- Facial hair thickens.
- Boys may have to begin shaving their facial hair.

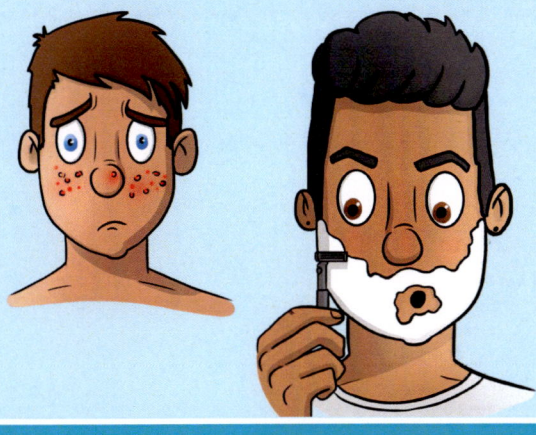

8   Physical Changes in Boys

- Most boys will reach full adult maturity by 18 years of age.

Changes in Females

9 Physical Changes in Girls

Part 1:

- Breasts start to grow.
- Pubic hair grows around the genitals.
- Growth spurt.

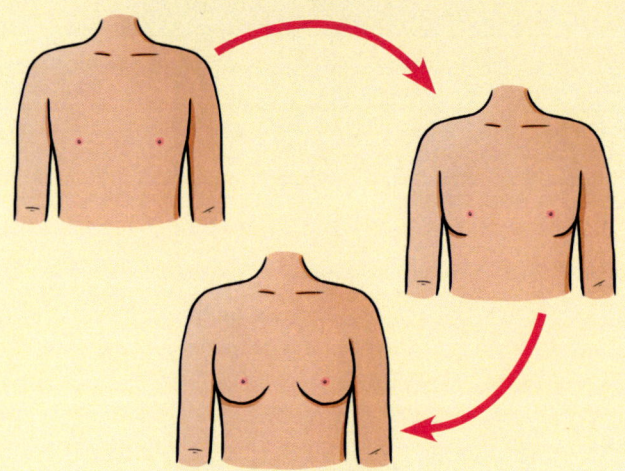

10 Physical Changes in Girls

Part 2:

- Breasts develop more.
- Hair under arms.
- Acne.
- Second growth spurt.

11 Physical Changes in Girls

Part 3:

- Eggs start to develop.
- Hips widen.
- Menstruation (periods) begin.

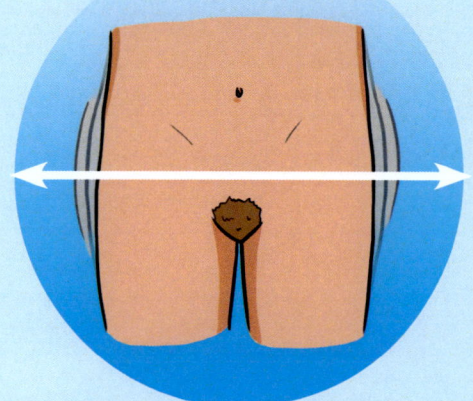

12 Mood Swings

- With puberty, some boys and girls will get **mood swings** and can be **grumpy**.

- Problems with parents and friends are **common**.

Feelings & Responsibility

13 Responsibility

- As a young adult, you have more say in what you do.

- Laws take more effect as you mature.

- You have more personal **responsibility** for your own actions.

14 Feelings

- New feelings arrive too.

- These feelings can be **confusing**.

Am I Normal?

15 Attraction

- Often you become **attracted to others**.

- This can be either for the opposite sex or the same sex.

- This is **normal**!

16 Be Confident!

- You have the right to say **no** to anything you do not want to do!

- **You should not be pressured** into physical, sexual or dangerous acts by friends or adults.

NO means NO

Get Advice

17 You and the Law

- The **age of sexual consent** for mixed and same sex relationships is **16 years**.

- You need to **be aware of the consequences (con-see-qu-enn-ses) (results)** of your actions.

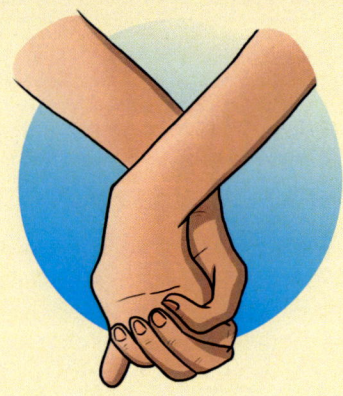

18 Advice!

- Remember that puberty is not forever!

- Things do settle.

- Friendships and relationships **improve** as you mature.

19 Advice!

- Remember that there is a long way to go before you are a full adult!

- Parents, teachers and carers all have been through it.

- They have advice to offer and an ear to listen with.

20 The Female Reproductive System

- The female **reproductive system** is a **group of organs** and tissues.

- They work together to carry out many functions.

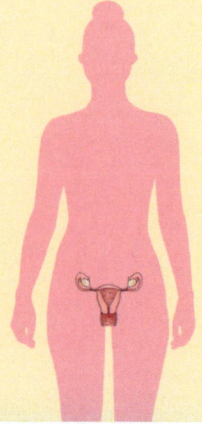

Female Reproduction System

21 The Female Reproductive System

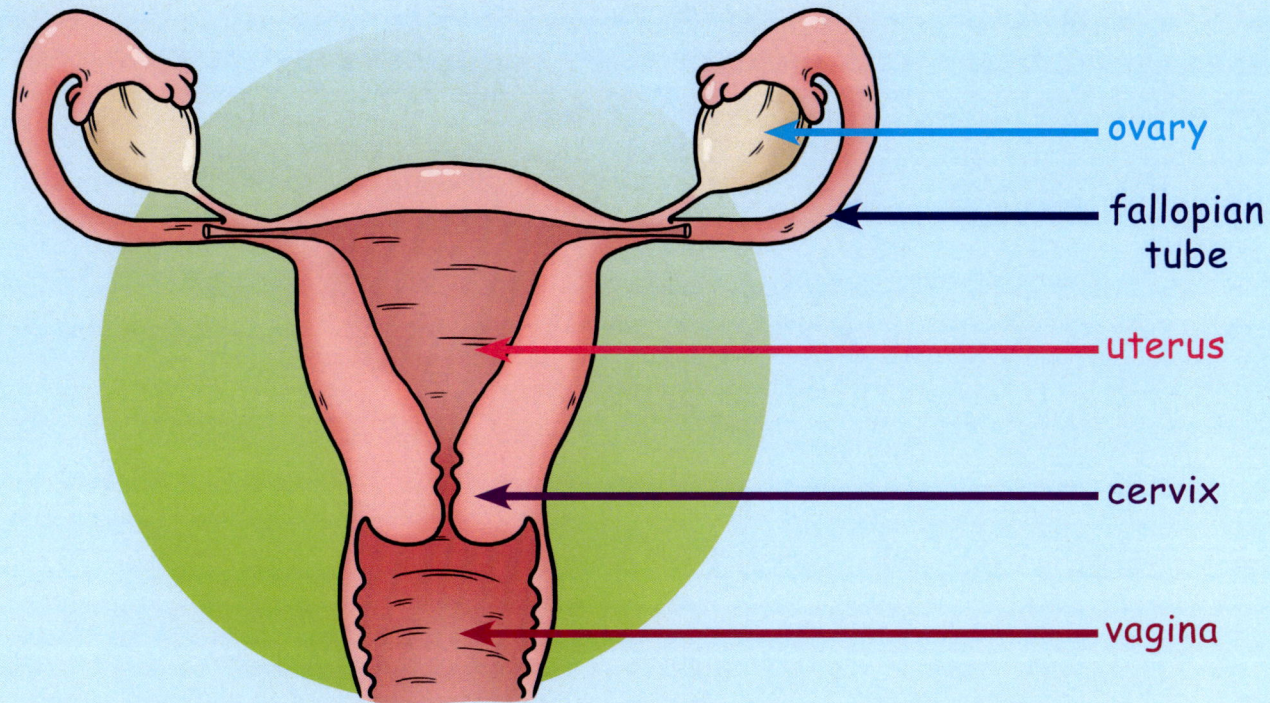

- ovary
- fallopian tube
- uterus
- cervix
- vagina

22 The Functions

The functions of the reproductive system are:

- **Producing human egg cells.**

- **Providing an environment** for the baby to grow.

- **Providing a** way for the baby to be born.

23 Side View

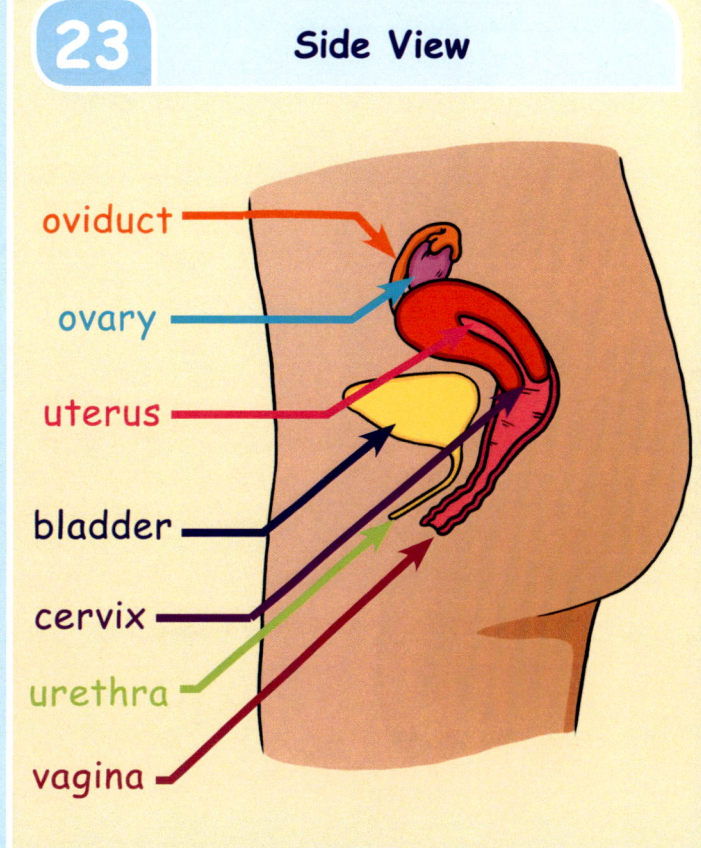

- oviduct
- ovary
- uterus
- bladder
- cervix
- urethra
- vagina

Female Reproduction System

24 Ovaries

- The **ovary** is an organ where **individual egg cells grow.**

- They develop from **early teenage years** to about **fifty years old.**

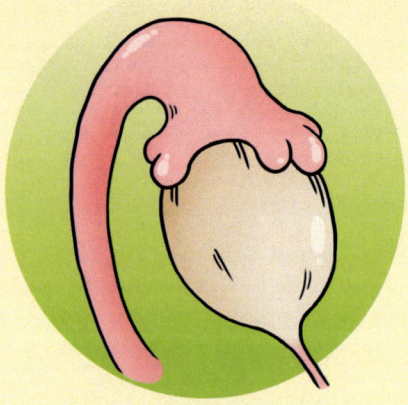

25 Oestrogen

- The ovary releases the sex hormone, **oestrogen.**

- This **starts menstruation.**

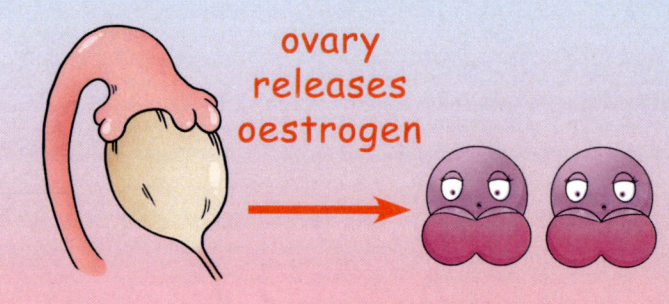

ovary releases oestrogen

26 Human Egg Cell

- A **human egg cell** is the **largest single cell** in the human body.

- It is just about visible with the naked eye.

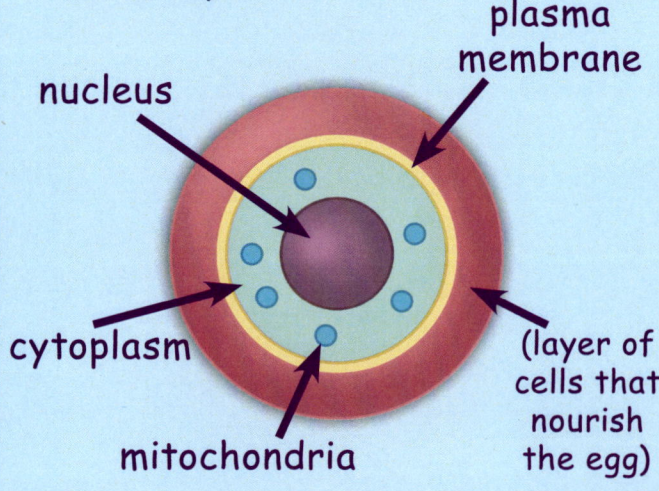

plasma membrane

nucleus

cytoplasm

mitochondria

(layer of cells that nourish the egg)

27 Human Egg Cell

- It **carries half of the genetic information** for a baby.

- This is the mother's half.

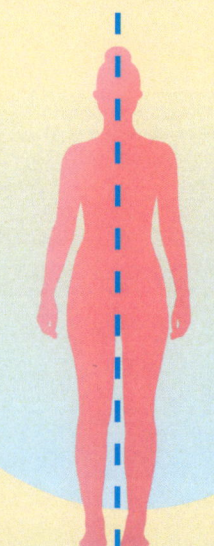

Female Reproduction System

28 Fallopian Tube / Oviduct

- The **fallopian tube** (also known as the **oviduct**) **carries the egg** from the **ovary** to the **uterus**.

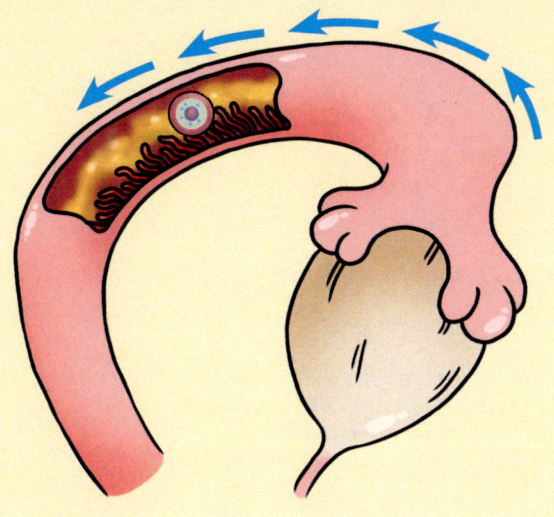

29 Fallopian Tube / Oviduct

- It is lined with **specialised cells** called **cilia**.

- These are **hair-like projections** which move together.

- They waft the egg from the ovary towards the uterus.

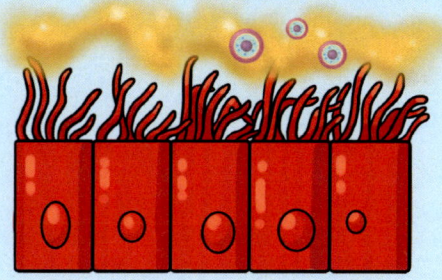

30 The Uterus

- The **uterus** is a muscular organ.

- It is about the size of a pear.

- It **is where a fetus** develops and grows.

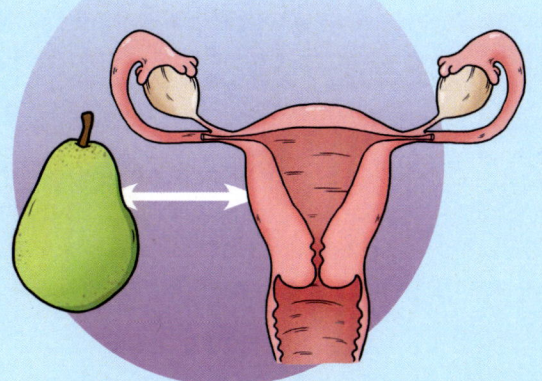

31 The Lining

- The lining of the uterus is called the **endometrium**.

- Each **month** the endometrium gets ready for the **fertilised egg** to arrive.

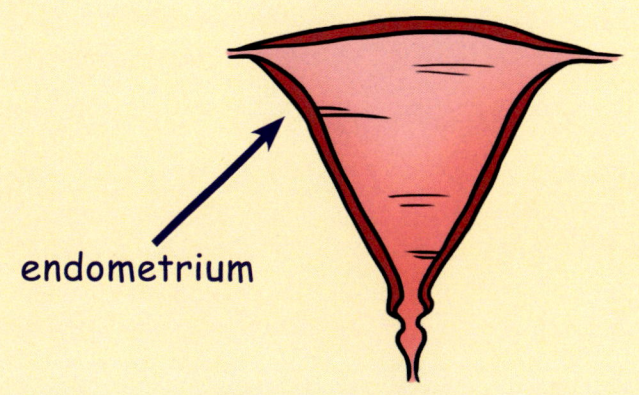

endometrium

Female Reproduction System

32   The Cervix

- The **cervix** is a tough cone of muscle.

- It is normally **closed** and helps support a growing unborn baby.

- It **relaxes at birth**. The uterine contractions push the baby through it.

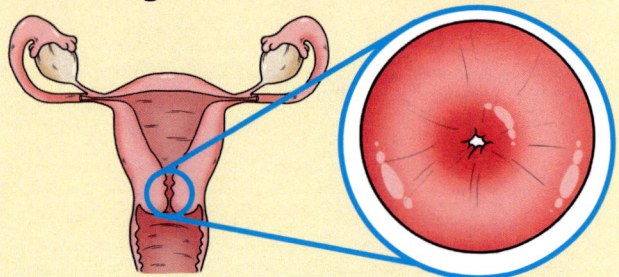

33   The Vagina

- The **vagina** is a muscular tube.

- This is where the penis enters during sex.

- It has has **weak acidic secretions** to help protect against infections.

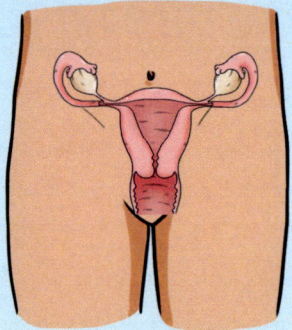

34   The Vulva

- The **vulva** is the **external** part of female genitals.

- It is **folds of tissue** covering the opening of the **vagina** and **urethra** (the tube from the bladder).

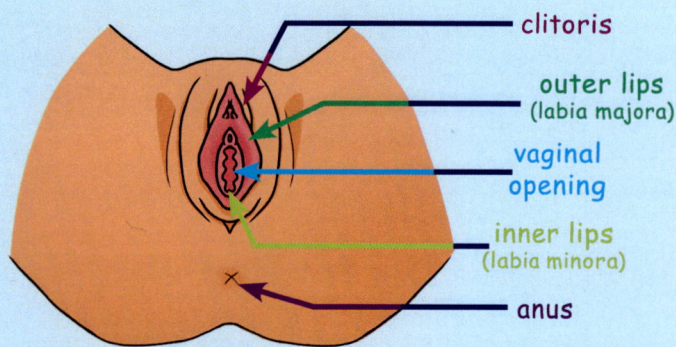

clitoris
outer lips (labia majora)
vaginal opening
inner lips (labia minora)
anus

35   Menstruation

- Menstruation occurs **every month** from puberty, until menopause (where eggs stop being released).

- If the egg is **not** fertilised, it will **leave the body** during menstruation.

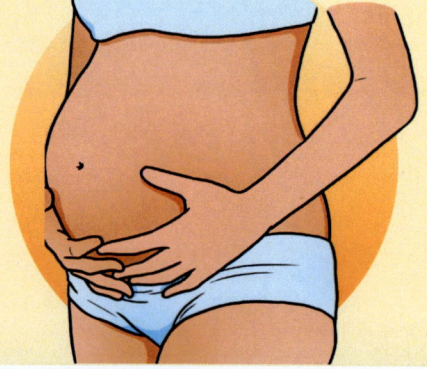

Male Reproduction System

36   The Male Reproductive System

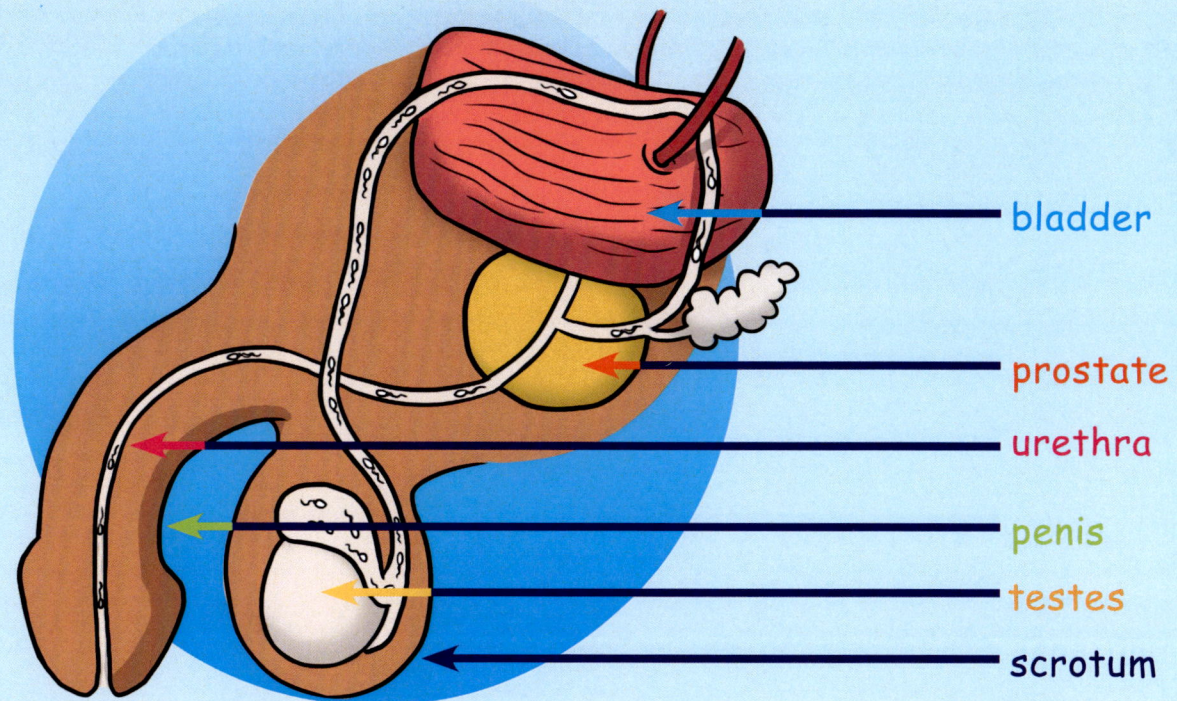

- bladder
- prostate
- urethra
- penis
- testes
- scrotum

37   Testes

- The **testes** are found behind the penis.

- They are found in a sac of skin called the scrotum.

- The **testes release testosterone** and **make sperm cells**.

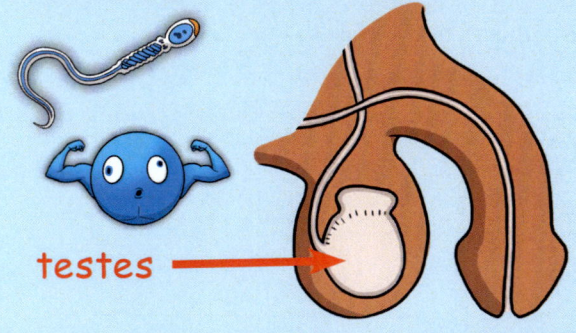

testes

38   Sperms Cells

- Sperm cells have the other **half of genetic information** needed to create a new baby.

- This genetic information comes from the **father**.

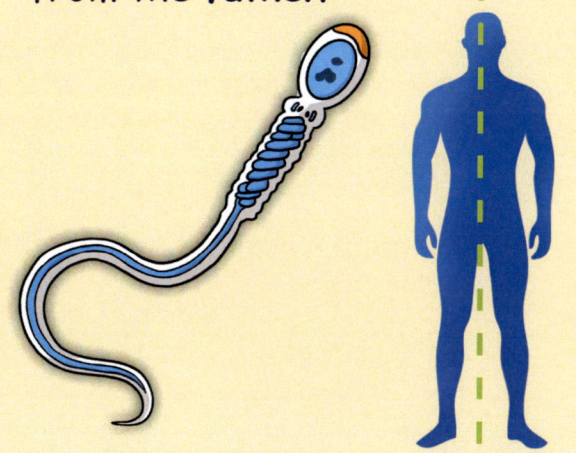

Male Reproduction System

39   Sperm Cells

- Sperm cells have **tails** to help them **swim** to the egg.

- The **mitochondria** in sperm cells, **releases energy** to help them swim.

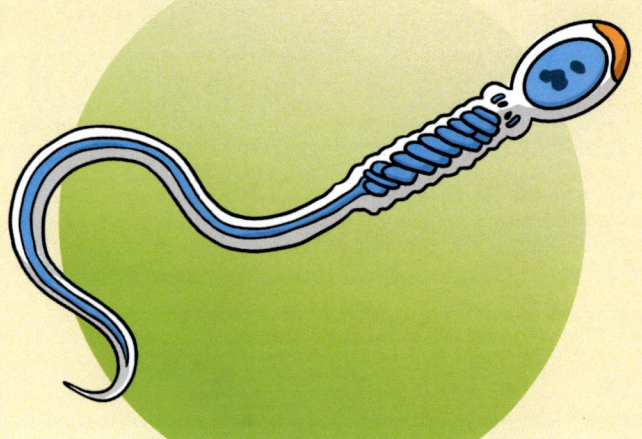

40   Head of the Sperm

- In the **head** of the sperm cells, there are **receptors**.

- These find the **hormones** within the egg.

- It also has **chemicals** that break through the wall of the egg.

- This is so it can **fertilise** the egg.

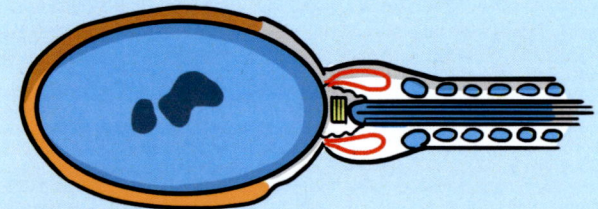

41   Ejaculation

- Over **100 million** sperm cells are produced every day in the testes!

- These cells are stored in the **epididymis**.

- There are **300 - 500 million** sperm cells in **one ejaculation**.

42   Move On Up!

- Sperm move up the **sperm duct** from the epididymis.

- Fluids are added from different **glands**.

- The **seminal vesicles** add a **sugary solution**.

- This is an **energy** source for the sperm.

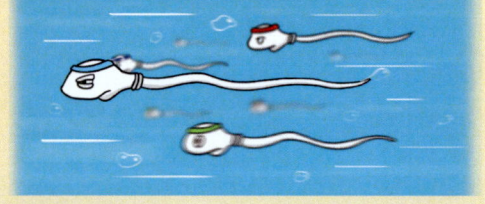

Sexual Intercourse

43 Semen

- The **prostate gland** adds an **alkali solution.**

- This **neutralizes** the acid in the **vagina.**

- This gives the sperm more chance to **survive.**

- When the sperm and solution mix, it is called **semen.**

44 Sexual Intercourse

- During sexual arousal the tissue within the penis **fills with blood.**

- It becomes **erect.**

- The erect penis is put into the vagina during **sexual intercourse.**

- **Semen** is then **ejaculated** into the **vagina.**

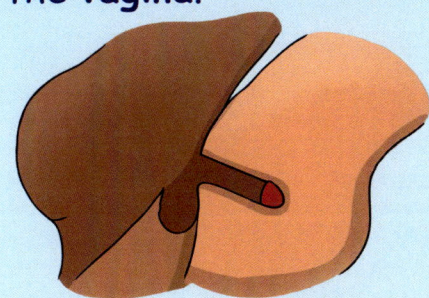

45 Sexual Intercourse

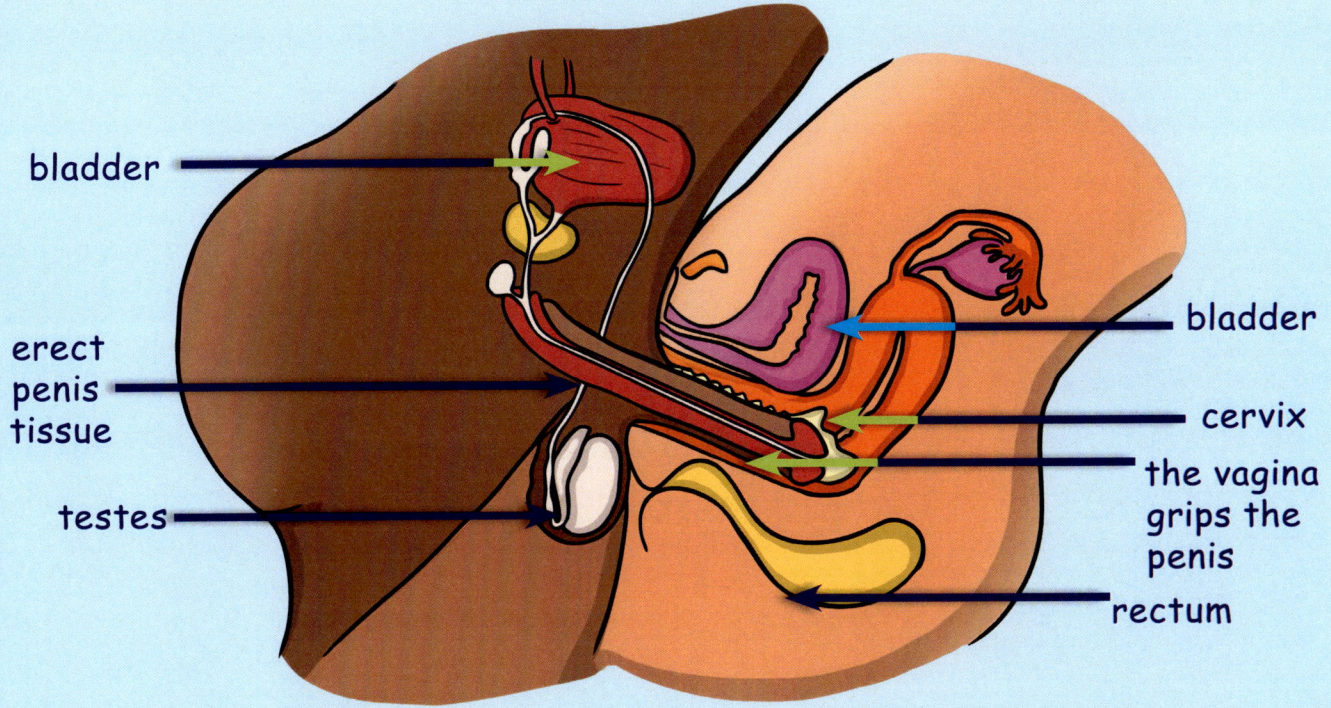

bladder

erect
penis
tissue

testes

bladder

cervix

the vagina
grips the
penis

rectum

Fertilisation

46   Just Keep Swimming...

- When ejaculated into the vagina, sperm cells begin to swim.

- The sperm move in **random directions**.

- Some pass through the **cervix** and enter the **fallopian tubes**.

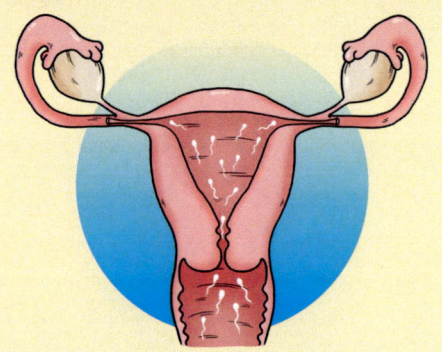

47   Fertilisation

- If an egg has been **released from an ovary** during sexual intercourse, **fertilisation** can happen.

- **Fertilisation** is when a sperm cell **fuses** (joins) with a human egg cell.

- This happens in the **fallopian tube**.

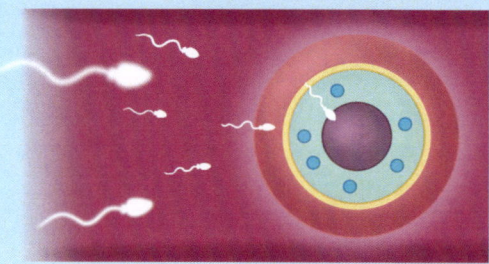

48   Zygote

- When the egg and the sperm cell fuse together, the new cell is called a **zygote**.

- The zygote moves towards the **uterus**.

- As it moves, it makes a **ball of cells**. This is called a **blastocyst**.

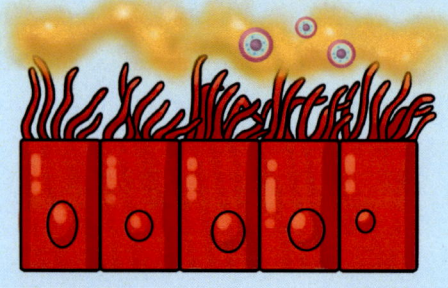

49   Implantation

- The **blastocyst** reaches the uterus. It **implants** itself into the **uterus wall**.

- This is where it **develops into** the **embyro** and then **the fetus**.

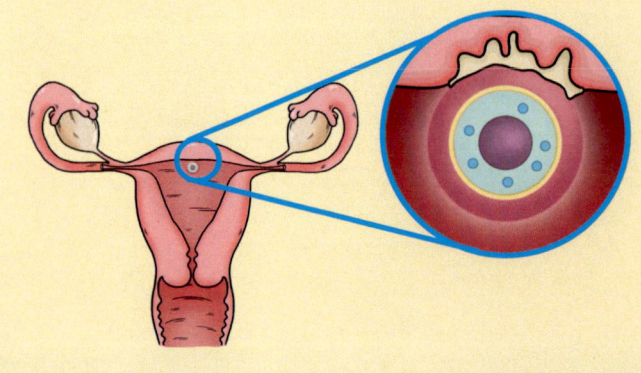

Pregnancy

50   Amnion

- For **42 weeks,** the **fetus** is carried in the **mother.**

- A fluid-filled sac called the **amnion** helps the baby.

- It **supports and protects** the growth of the baby.

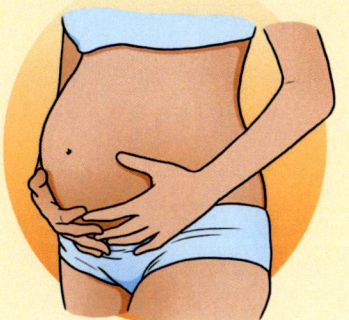

51   The Placenta

- The **placenta exchanges substances** between the mother's and the unborn baby's blood.

- However, their blood never mixes!

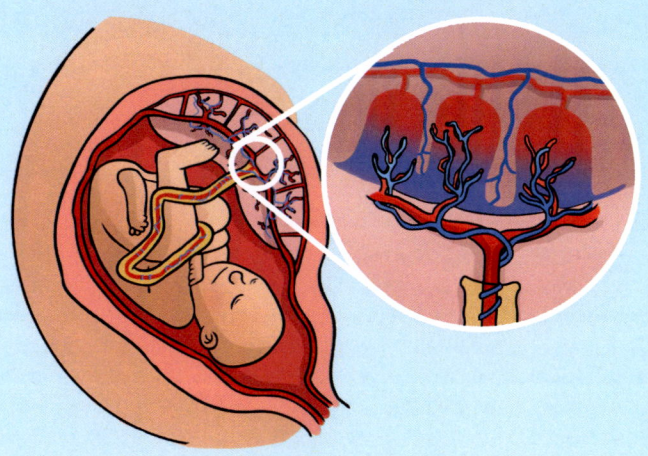

52   Nutrients and Waste!

- **Oxygen** and **nutrients** are passed through the **umbilical vein.**

- They go **into** the **baby's blood** in the placenta.

- These substances come **from** the **mother's blood.**

- This helps the baby to **develop and grow.**

- **Waste** products, like carbon dioxide, **leave** the baby through the **umbilical artery.**

- The waste moves across into the mother's blood at the **placenta.**

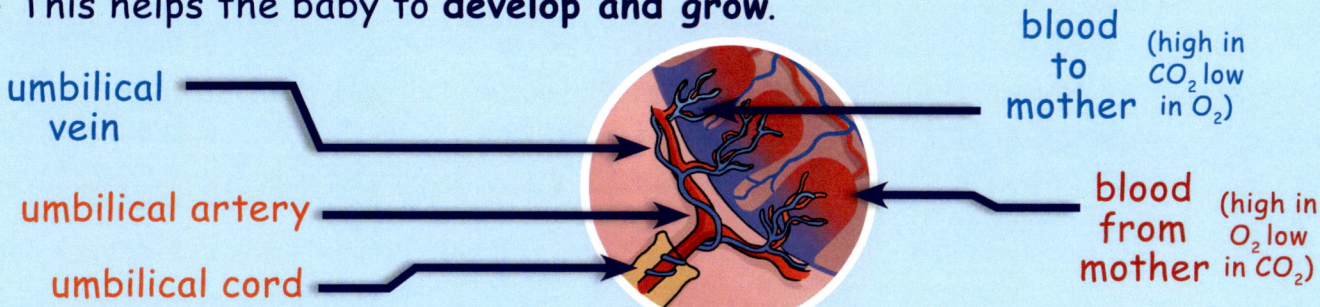

umbilical vein

umbilical artery

umbilical cord

blood to mother (high in CO_2 low in O_2)

blood from mother (high in O_2 low in CO_2)

Pregnancy

53 — Looking After The Unborn Baby

- Smoking, drinking and taking drugs can harm an unborn baby.

- Mothers need a healthy diet and lifestyle for their unborn baby to grow.

54 — Giving Birth

- Babies can be born early.

- Babies born **before** 37 weeks are called **premature**.

- The earlier they are born the more at risk they are.

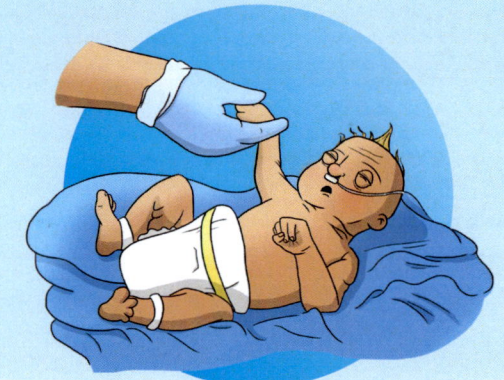

55 — Coming Out!

- Babies are usually born **head first**!

- **Hormones** in the mother and baby **start the birth**.

- The uterus begins to **contract**.

- This pushes the baby through the **vagina**.

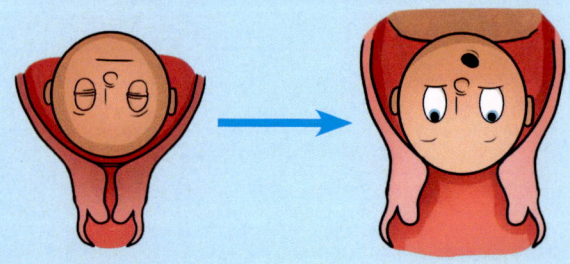

56 — The Afterbirth

- Contractions still carry on to deliver the **placenta** (or **afterbirth**).

- The contractions help the uterus to return to its normal size.

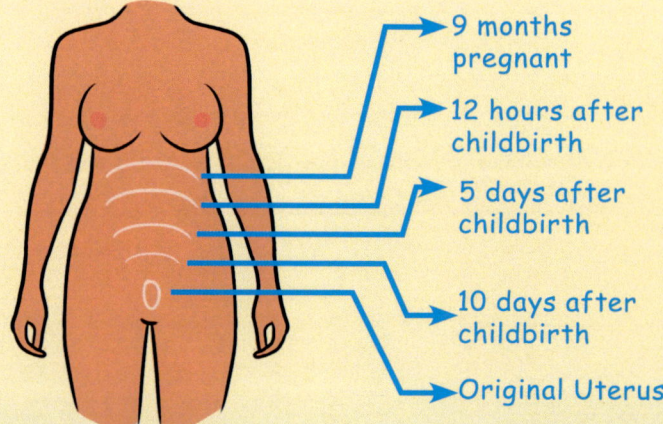

9 months pregnant

12 hours after childbirth

5 days after childbirth

10 days after childbirth

Original Uterus

This booklet is not to be photocopied. Thank you.

Menstruation Cycle
(This is usually a 28 day cycle)

Days 1 - 4

- If the egg is not fertilised, it will be bled out.
- This happens monthly.

Days 5 - 13

- The cells of the uterus lining thicken.
- The blood flow increases.

Menstrual Cycle

- Fertile Days
- menstruation

				1	2	3
4	5	6	7	8	9	10
11	12	13	14	15	16	17
18	19	20	21	22	23	24
25	26	27	28			

uterus lining thickens

MAINTENANCE IN PROGRESS

Days 17 - 28

- Hormones maintain the lining of the uterus.
- This is in case an egg is fertilised.
- After this the menstruation cycle goes back to day 1.

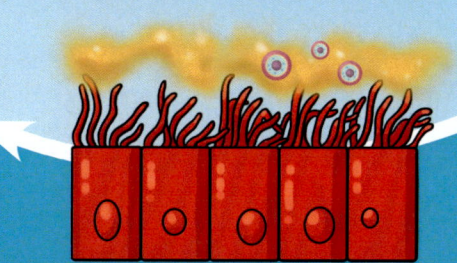

Days 14 - 17

- A mature egg is released from the ovary into the fallopian tube before it moves towards the uterus.
- If the woman has intercourse, she is likely to get pregnant during this time.

About Oaka Books

Children learn best when they are engaged...

Our aim is to help children enjoy learning by making it fun! That way they will succeed.

Following Common Entrance and National Curriculum guidelines for KS3.

Design and layout of our books follow guidelines from the British Dyslexia Association

Three Easy Steps

Read: the easy to follow bullet point Topic Booklet.

Engage: Play the Active Learning Game.

Learn: When you understand the topic, test yourself using the Write Your Own Notes Book. You can use the Topic Booklet to help if you get stuck.

One (short) Topic at a time:

For some students, a big book is a big turn off. That's why we focus on one topic at a time. Short and to the point.

Reading Age

This booklet is suitable for children with a reading age of 10 ½ years.

Topic Packs for KS1, KS2 & KS3 Include:

History
Geography
Chemistry
Biology
Physics

Please visit www.oakabooks.co.uk for more information about forthcoming titles

© Copyright 2017 Oaka Books. All rights reserved. Written by Su McRae Bsc (Hons), PGCE (Bath). Illustrations by Laurence Andrew Page & Adora Holcroft.

First paperback edition printed 2015 in the United Kingdom.
A catalogue record for this book is available from the British Library.

ISBN 978-1-909892-75-0
No part of this book shall be reproduced or transmitted in any form or by any means, electronic or mechanical, including photocopying, recording or by any information retrieval system without written permission of the copyright owner or a licence permitting restricted copying issued by the Copyright Licensing Agency Ltd, Saffron House, 6-10 Kirby Street, London EC1N 8TS Tel: 020 7400 3100   Fax: 020 7400 3101   Email: cla@cla.co.uk   Web: www.cla.co.uk

Designed, set and published by Oaka™ Books.

To order other titles from Oaka™ Books, please email info@oakabooks.co.uk or visit www.oakabooks.co.uk, or phone: +44 (0) 2392 388519.

Acknowledgements
Our huge thanks go to the many teachers who have been involved in the development of this series of learning guides. Special thanks to Joy Gardiner, for producing hundreds of illustrations, to Kate Doehren, for her enthusiasm and invaluable assistance to my wonderful daughter Sophie, for being the inspiration for the books and, of course, to Charlie, for believing in them.

ISBN 978-1-909892-75-0

Produced in association with Kate Doehren, MA Ed, B.Ed Hons, RSA Dip, Sp LD/Dyslexia
Director of Learning Support, Hurstpierpoint College
© Copyright Oaka™ Books 2018

ISBN 978-1-909892-75-0
9 781909 892750

OB7C27
Puberty, Reprodu...
Topic Booklet